Brilliant Rhymes

Edited By Jenni Harrison

First published in Great Britain in 2020 by:

Young Writers
Remus House
Coltsfoot Drive
Peterborough
PE2 9BF
Telephone: 01733 890066
Website: www.youngwriters.co.uk

Printed and bound in the UK by BookPrintingUK
Website: www.bookprintinguk.com
YB0446KX

FOREWORD

Here at Young Writers our defining aim is to promote the joys of reading and writing to children and young adults and we are committed to nurturing the creative talents of the next generation. By allowing them to see their own work in print we believe their confidence and love of creative writing will grow.

Out Of This World is our latest fantastic competition, specifically designed to encourage the writing skills of primary school children through the medium of poetry. From the high quality of entries received, it is clear that it really captured the imagination of all involved.

We are proud to present the resulting collection of poems that we are sure will amuse and inspire.

An absorbing insight into the imagination and thoughts of the young, we hope you will agree that this fantastic anthology is one to delight the whole family again and again.

CONTENTS

Joseph Lyons (10)	126	Amelia Spahia	172
Isabelle May Wooldridge (10)	127	Zayan Hussain (10)	173
Harrison Darwin (10)	128	Maanav Nagda (11)	174
George Unwin (9)	130	Leila Smith (9)	175
Akshaya Jeyaseelan (10)	131	Fatima Akmal (8)	176
Zak Gandhi (11)	132	Matvei Nepomnjastsih	177
Luke Turner (8)	134	Khadijah Iman (8)	178
Dylan Jones (10)	135	Xander Weston (8)	179
Ava Cassandra Goshei (10)	136	Rashvin	180
Roshan Merani (10)	138	Malakaai Luke Steele (11)	181
Anne Appiah-Sarpong (10)	139	Teddy Epstein (10)	182
Imogen Little (9)	140	Yahia Abdulgawad (7)	183
Ankhan Aswani (8)	141	Rayan Anderson (9)	184
Eliza Noor Bhatti (8)	142	Olivia Peddle (11)	185
Alexandra Slavova	143	Chudi Patrick Onwuokwu (9)	186
Shiven Bhudia (10)	144	Shayaan Noman (8) & Safa	187
Krishan Dodhia (8)	145	Ashrit Marti (11)	188
Andre Henri Josse (8)	146	Aarya Goenka (10)	189
Emmett Michael Hugh	147	Maryam Hooria Maqsood (10)	190
Lawson (10)		Riya Boominathan (8)	191
William Nicolson (8)	148	Harry Fielden (8)	192
Andrew MacDonald (10)	149	Emma Timis (10)	193
Poppy Hunt (10)	150	Amar Maan (10)	194
Isabella Vincent-Pink (8)	151	Razi Shabeeh (7)	195
Abu-Bakr Ismail (10)	152	Sam Toffel (7)	196
Troy Dennis (9)	153	Khushi Rohit (6)	197
Jack Timis (10)	154	Lily-May Spence (8)	198
Louis Emile Josse (11)	155	Oliwia Zborowska (10)	199
Alice Seaman (9)	156	Neive Sarah Homewood (11)	200
Dolly Parsons (11)	158	Sumayyah Ayub	201
Javier J Cabrera (9)	159	Daniel Park (10)	202
Katherine Serrano (11)	160	Evangeline Goodwin (8)	203
Hope Morton	161	Yixing Chen (9)	204
Gibran Karim Khan (11)	162	Ali Mian (7)	205
Hannah Ismail (6)	163	Amber Williamson-Brown (9)	206
Lisshan Rasakumaran (10)	164	Aarush Marti (8)	207
Adele Aman Dosalieva (9)	165	Anujan Nirubaraj (9)	208
Jessica Smart (8)	166	Mohammed Sulevani (10)	209
Aryaan Mahmood (9)	167	Fareed Ahmed (6)	210
Aysha Afridi (11)	168	Muhmmad Ayub (9)	211
Abarnaya Jeyaseelan (10)	169	Finn Gooding (8)	212
Shyaama Modha (11)	170	Mariam Khan (14)	213
Ione Greenstock (10)	171	Tiger Eaton (6)	214

Louie Trett (7)	215
Sianna Cooper (10)	216
Harvey Goodsell	217
Madison Porter	218
Anujan Nirubaraj (9)	219
Charlie West (7)	220
Shannon Carol Briggs (11)	221
Rosie Shindler (8)	222
Oreoluwapo Faseha (10)	223
Jayden Tomlinson (11)	224
Davina Bajwa (11)	225
Celio Carreiro-Lee (9)	226
Amr Abdulgawad (10)	227
Monica Bajwa (9)	228
Elsha Jom (8)	229
Kayla Thompson (9)	230

THE POEMS

Ride Of Your Life

It was the day of the launch. Sitting at the top, was I scared? Not much. The static crackled in my ear over the intercom. "Strap in, Soyuz is about to launch."

My crewmate started flicking switches and... off we went. Lifting off from Kazakhstan to the ISS. I felt the G loads piling on my chest.

"The space station is to the west," I said. "But wait a minute," I called to Ned who was sitting next to me. "I need a wee, take the controls and fly us to safety."

But as Ned leant over my controls a light flashed, we had gone too far. With the thrusters stuck and out of luck we sailed past the sun. Ned said, "Not fun," as we sling-shotted around the star.

I exclaimed, "Earth isn't far, even in a car." Soon we were on a trajectory to re-entry. The heat built up around. I said, "I hope we get found." After that the parachute opened. We were safe and sound.

Sam Allcorn (11)

Trapped In A Bubble

I am trapped in a bubble.
Gallons of rules and
Chores making trouble.
"How can they make trouble?"
I hear you ask,
Well,
When people are given,
A chore, rule or task,
They get annoyed,
So they try to ignore it.
The rule-maker wants,
To be obeyed,
So they get not a bit,
But very, very angry,
When you refuse.
And if they decide,
To tell you off,
It is like they have pulled a trigger,
Then the problem just gets bigger and bigger,

I am trapped in a bubble.
Especially when,

I see my friends,
I have to keep them,
Happy and subtle,
Before our whole,
Friendship ends.
It's hard to be friends,
With everyone,
And still not make,
Any friendship groups done,
Also, it's very,
Difficult when,
Your enemy tries,
To be your friend,
And everybody accepts them but you,
You try to pretend, but it's hard, cos it's new,

I am trapped in a bubble.
Cos I try so,
Hard to be nice,
And to not lose my temper,
To not be mean or disliked,
Or to get even grumpier,
Grumpier then whoever,

Seems to get you ready,
Ready to insult them,
Or get them ready,
To leave you alone,
With your real friends,
Or your dog,
(Although he is chewing a bone)
At least your dog is better than that friend,
Your dog will be beside you till the end,

I am trapped in a bubble.
Rebounding off the sides,
From rule wall 1,
To rule wall 3,
To chore door 5,
To chore door 16,
And back to,
Rule wall 1,
To that horrid friend,
Before I reach the end,
I whizz past that,
Happiness spark,

Crash into Noah,
And his ark,
But of course this is now,
Imaginary,
I'm in a dream world,
Where things become scary,
I look around,
And see that I've
Woken up first,
I'm back in real life,
Back in the bubble and so I then,
Roll my eyes, and start again.

Heidi Arnold

Argument Of The Planets

Imagine that the planets can talk,
They're having quite a row.
Because you see they like to think
They're each the best somehow.

First we hear from Pluto:
"I'm furthest from the sun.
I'm a beautiful blue and it's also true
That I'm the smallest one!"

Mercury is listening,
And disagrees somewhat.
"You can't really compete here as
A real planet you are not!"

"I am now the smallest,
So I win that hands down!"
"Hey, what's the fuss about being small?"
Raises Jupiter with a frown.

"Surely being largest
Is something to revere.

Plus more moons spin around me
Than anybody here."

A grin spread right across his face
Until Saturn had his say.
"The scientists discovered more moons
Around me the other day!"

Saturn continued on, "Besides
You'll find I have a ring.
Made of bright yellow and orange gas,
'Tis quite a stunning thing!"

Neptune shouted, "I'm the coldest!"
The others could barely hear.
He was the furthest one away
By several light-years.

Venus screamed, "Well I'm the hottest,
And I'm the brightest one!"
Mercury chipped in, "That may be,
But I'm closest to the sun!"

"I'm the one with the funniest name!"
Can you guess whose voice this was?

Yes, you would be absolutely right,
This one was Uranus!

It was Mars' turn to state his case,
"Dust storms occur on me.
I am the Roman God of War,
That scores some points, surely!"

A hush descended, no sound was heard.
The planets had all spoken.
Apart from just one, green and blue,
Who'd kept quiet through all the commotion.

Now Earth began to speak aloud,
"I've made a judgement call.
The writer of this poem lives on me,
So I just beat you all!"

Ollie Slatkin (10)

The Truth About The Wacky Melon Monster

I was home from school. It was a hectic day at school. All of a sudden I heard a noise coming from on top of the tree, so I walked faster and was petrified. Suddenly, a huge monster appeared... he was as chubby as a big balloon. His arms were longer than the distance to the sun. He had forty pink eyes.

"Please don't eat me."

"I've come for your hands. I'll eat them in just one gobble up..."

"Um, but why do you have flower pants on your head?"

"Oh I forgot to take them off my washing line."

He had a washing line on his head, between his two antennae...

"I know, let's make a deal. I'll let you use my washing line if you eat my teacher's hands. They're much more sweatier."

"Okay, you've got a deal." And off he went to gobble up the teacher's hands and off I went home again after a hectic day.

Iqrah Raja (9)

Won't You Save Me?

I am near my mother amidst towering Australian
trees
When I see something flickering in the distance,
something unknown to me,
It blazes bright colours, wearing robes of orange
and red
My mother scooped me up in her pouch and
bounced straight ahead
There were clouds of smoke and ash, as well as
intense heat
My mother and I didn't know what we'd meet,
Humans shouted, "Flames! Fire!"
And it was licking and burning our home at its
heart's desire
As we turned back my mother's tail just caught the
flame
But she hopped all the while, ignoring the pain,
The fire confronted us and circled us all around
So my mother leaped, ending hard on the ground
But in the leap I'd fallen to the leaf-covered earth
Where was my protection I'd had since birth?
She hadn't noticed and disappeared among the
wood

So the fire started gripping me, smoke covering me like a hood
Humans burst through the flames, I thought they'd save me
I hopped their way, but they were saving a koala from a tree,
"A baby kangaroo here," I squealed, but they hadn't heard
So they rescued the koala and left without a word

I hopped out of the gaps that the humans made
And I found my mother, running out of the shade,
I chased after her, she saw me and her face changed from worry to delight
So she picked me up and hugged me with all her might
I hope that humans sort out the problem of fire
So we can live safely anywhere at our heart's desire,
Remember, humans, you are not the only ones who care
God made this Earth so we could all have our own share.

Arna Kar (12)

The Enchanted Forest

I stealthily came out to see if the rumours were
true
Is there an enchanted forest coming out of the
blue?
I quickly crept out, my walk became a run
And at a leisurely pace, up went the sun

My eyes came into focus, trees were pink and red
Diamonds hung above me, as I looked ahead
Unicorns were there, as far as the eye could see
At a moment's notice, I saw one was with me

To see all the sights, I stared everywhere
The wind blew a breeze, it played with my hair
Quicker than light, a griffin lifted me in the sky
It was a different euphoria, being up so high

I instantly realised, diamonds brushed against my
face
As soon as the griffin saw this, it increased its pace
The griffin was taking me to a spot of hidden
treasure
There were so many riches, it was impossible to
measure

A songbird flew up to me, it chirped what it said,
"Danger! Danger! Dragon up ahead!"
The unicorn galloped rapidly, it soon snuck me in
I gasped as soon as I saw the contents within.

The unicorn said, "Go and get the pot,"
"We have a lot of everything, but time we have
not."
I soon grasped the vessel and the unicorn took me
out

The animals stayed silent, though happy they
didn't shout

I gave the pot to the griffin who quickly flew away
When the songbird saw this, it shouted, "Hooray!"
I got on the unicorn who took me to my house
It quickly went along, quiet as a mouse

I had experienced something beyond my wildest
dreams
Though, to find the forest is not as easy as it seems
Now I had the knowledge, the rumours were true
There was an enchanted forest coming out of the
blue.

Srilakshmi Seshadri (10)

My Town

If you are small and shy
You are strong

If you are big and brave
You are weak

It's upside down
In my town
And it's the happiest town
That will ever be

We live in peace
And all forgive

No one ever disagrees
In my town
And no one ever searches
For a crown

It's all friendly
It's all part of honesty

This is a merry song
This is not wrong

For there is justice
In my town

If you are small and shy
You are strong

If you are big and brave
You are weak

This town holds the future with glory

Respect, responsibility
Co-operation and resilience
Is what we are looking for

But not in our town
Cos our town already has that

So we are looking for something new
We are looking for adventures
That are due in our lives

The size does not matter
For not all of us follow our say

If you are small and shy
You are strong

If you are big and brave
You are weak

It's upside down
In my town
And it's the happiest town
That will ever be

This is all I have to say
About my marvellous town
And that I am grateful
For this life.

Elisa Mineo (11)

Are We Ready To Fly?

The two best friends building something great
Their names are Tom and Kate
"Are we ready to fly?" shouted Tom, speeding around the rainbow plane
"Let's do this!" exclaimed Kate, thinking about going to Spain
Ready to fly they bounced into the spectacular plane and flew to the sky
Flying straight up it looked like a lie
Boom! Crash! Smash! Stuck on the shard and definitely not in Canada (or Spain) they were stuck
Aeroplanes flew everywhere nearly crashing into them even cars and trucks
Unfortunately, a car hit them and like a ballerina they came twirling down
Both sadly frowned
Until, *bounce!* The plane jumped on someone's car
They flew up high and they could see far
Backflipped back home, the exhausted kids finally arrived home
And the kids only wanted ice cream in a cone.

Dimeari Ibiama (10)

When The Caged Bird Sings

When the caged bird sings, the sun will rise and
will bathe our sins in light.
The ice caps will not cry wet tears with every
motion, nor sink to the bottom of the ocean.
Polar bears won't seek for shelter or hide in the
night.
When the caged bird sings, everything will be
alright.

When the caged bird sings, the moon will observe
us: "What a beautiful sight!"
And the forests will not weep for the great oak, nor
vanish beneath a polluted cloak.
The leaves will fall gracefully and crisp to their
moonlight path, flooded with sunlight.
When the caged bird sings, everything will be
alright.

When the caged bird sings, the sunset will be
scarlet red and the trees will gain tall height.
The bees won't vanish off the face of this earth,
nor die hungry on the pea-green turf.

They will fly in harmony: freedom is flight!
When the caged bird sings, everything will be
alright.

When the caged bird sings, people will learn better
than to fight.
Peace on this land and glory per every golden
sand.
No country will be blood-red, animals will be free
and all flags will be peace-white.
When the caged bird sings, humans and animals
will live as equals and everyone will hum:
"The caged bird is right!"

Ellie Todorova

Togetherness

Let's have a little look on the days around us all
This will help you get straight back up whenever
you fall
Some days bring sunshine, some bring rain
But we can fix things up and feel ourselves again
Because in this life we are all unique
So never change and always speak
Speak of happy, good and bad
Use your voice and don't be sad
For all in this world that we have to give
Is our own life our right to live
As we grow things around us may change
Our surroundings and lifestyles will rearrange
But always remember you are your own
And in this world you are never alone
The people all around us they are all different too
We are all our own person only you can only be
you
People may judge and not be very nice
But do not listen to negatives, take this advice
Love yourself from deep within

Always keep your beautiful grin
If you ever may feel low
Just show off your smile, stand up and glow
And always remember that you'll always find
Good things happen so long as you're kind
Now close your eyes and have a little rest
And tomorrow go give it your very best
Share happiness everywhere and watch others
smile
For bad days only come every once in a while.

Ella-May McCarroll (9)

Into My Bedroom Closet

If you would enter my bedroom closet,
Away from my crafted comets,
You would be amazed what would happen!

A magical portal would open up,
And you would see a tiger cub.

Its mother would be *very* angry!
So don't hesitate step in,
Don't be scared just grin,
Close your eyes,
I'm not telling lies.

You see...
The portal would suck you up,
Into the Milky Way galaxy!
A pool of chocolate is what you'll spectate,
It's a shame there is no chocolate cake.

Little goblins as green as grass,
Will be playing some sort of brass.
A gargantuan space monster will take a look,
Don't worry he's *not* a very good cook!

"You shouldn't be here, where should you be?"
He did say, staring right at me.
Don't worry he's not a frightening chap,
He will softly place you on his lap
"In my bedroom, fast asleep."
"I'll keep you don't worry," he said as soft as a sheep.

And so he will push you kindly into the portal
Just ready for my mum to call
"Maisy, Maisy are you sleeping?"
And not a peep I make, my face beaming.

Tomisin Joel (9)

Our Universe

Our universe is exquisite and full of awe-inspiring planets,
We all have spectacular views of landmarks made from granite.
Earth is full of wonderful creatures, lions, tigers and pumas,
As well as scrumptious fruits, from mangos and satsumas!

Venus is full of bright burning lava which oozes around the magnificent rocks,
Will there be wonderful creatures - just like on Earth - such as wolves or a red fox?
Earthquakes crumbling the land full of destruction - from cracks to black holes
Burning magma swirling out of control and forming obsidian poles.

Bitter and cold is our friend Neptune who is frosty and shimmers,
This delicate and delightful blue planet is full of ice that glimmers!

No land is as stunning as Neptune, in the distance all is quiet and calm,
Its formation is from a glacier ice palm.

Stunning Saturn with its rings is like the ultimate racing car track,
Walking around the rings step by step on the space path,
Its rings our like a battle arena,
Saturn is the size of a colossal field,

Our world is superb,
Our universe is gigantic and wonderful,
Our galaxy is phenomenal and outstanding,
Our whole world is stupendous.

Siddhant Shah (8)

Survivor

Ten years from now, where you and I may be
sitting,
Walking or sleeping, the world around us will have
changed.
Everywhere from beaches to parks for miles and
miles, plastic ranged.
Everyone and everything dead,
They never knew that their time would come to an
end.
Only one survived, and they knew what they had to
mend.
The survivor knew that the treacherous real World
War I wasn't a lost cause.
You see, over the time of humans, there were
many wars,
But none quite like this, for each side fuelled each
other's resources.
Humans needed plastic sources,
But they didn't treat their world right;
They littered day and night.
They made more and more,
But they never settled their score.

But now, plastic is an immense blanket that covers the world.
Humans tried to get rid of it, but the plastic unfurled.
Maybe in a world where humanity could be restarted,
And somewhere so silent you could hear someone breathing,
The survivor can save the world by making a little difference every day.
One small thing can make a huge impact on the plastic that's seething.
One day, the world will realise their mistake and the world will be okay.

Maia Raja (10)

United Verse

While Saturn flicked through a fashion magazine
Jupiter tried to cover her spot to look like a royal
queen
As Mars turned the heater to maximum five
Earth was trying to keep everyone alive
Mercury planted seeds in his craters
Neptune waited for his well-paid waiter
While Uranus was drinking medicine to get rid of
his flu
Venus started making a warm and welcoming
stew.

As the shooting star tried to fulfil its wishes
A little girl wished for many goldfishes
While the cheeky comets searched for their next
victim
The meteorites learnt a whole new system
The Milky Way devoured a Mars bar
As the satellite spied on the planets from afar
The gravity punched everyone to the ground
And the rocket bolted up with a noisy sound

Later, Pluto baked some delicious cupcakes
As the sun signed autographs near a crystal-clear
lake
The dwarf planets frolicked around in the
playground
While the galaxies checked their purses for at least
a pound.

Earth's moons waited patiently for his astronaut
guest
The black holes went to bed to take a rest
Then the universe waved its hearty goodbye
Since it was time for bedtime.

Ipar Kurban (9)

Ninja Fish

It was a nice sunny, relaxing day
Everyone was chilling out on the bay.
Sunbathing, building sandcastles, surfing
It was a day for lots of singing.

But under the sea it wasn't the same
Fishes not playing the same game.
All this mayhem caused by one fish
And that was... the Ninja Fish!

He had swords made out of shark teeth!
That he achieved as a big feat.
And suit made out of sea snake skin
And to scare other fish, a shark fin.

That day, he got the courage
To jump onto the sand with rage.
Then he could intimidate all
And play with the world, like a ball.

In a flash he ran near some jellyfish
And didn't notice their faces of anguish.

He swam up to the top of the sea
And saw a swarm of bees.

He swam to shore as quickly as he could
And picked up a piece of food.
Everyone froze and stared at him
Then ran off screaming, and sweating to the brim!

He ran to the sandcastles in a band
And broke them into just sand.
He grabbed an ice cream from the shop
And broke its cone in front of a shocked cop!

At last a brave boy came up to Ninja Fish
Scooped him up and ate him as a dinner dish!
So kids, don't do bad deeds
Else you will become a good man's feed!!

Riyansh Kirodian (10)

The Environment

The Earth is falling, life is fading
We need to help Mother Earth
Act now before it's too late
For this is our place of birth.

Remember to recycle what you use
A lot of it can be reused
Glass, paper, plastic and tin
Can all fit in your recycling bin.

Plastic floats across the ocean
Mixing together with toxic potions
The fish come by and eat it up
But then get a horrible feeling in their gut
If you see plastic in the street
Pick it up and give the Earth a treat.

There is litter all around us
There is litter under our feet
It blows into the ocean
Where it shouldn't be set free
Litter is everywhere apart from the bin
Where it should lie, either thick or thin.

Polluting, polluting and more polluting,
We need to stop polluting
Greenhouse gases and fossil fuels
Spread around like toxic fuels
Stop polluting or else the world will come to an
end
Wildlife will disappear and we will have no air to
breathe.

We need to help the environment whatever comes
our way
If we don't, there will be no night or day.

Aarav Radia (8)

Poetic Pigeon

The sky loomed over an ocean blue
And slowly lowered its once bright hue
Streetlights switched on
And cars came and gone
Late-night shows were on air
And Strictly dancers had a flair

But one small pigeon was perched on a tree
Wondering *can I do poetry?*
The next bright day she set out to the highest peak
Of the board of critiques
She rehearsed a poem with prosody
And knew that she was not a nobody.

Before she knew it, she was on stage
Only holding a page
Of the poem she rehearsed with heart
And people thought her smart
The critics were an owl, a fox, and a cat
With the scorer being a rat
She felt big and proud
As cheers erupted from the crowd

When she flew home
She expected her siblings to groan
As they didn't win
But they seemed to throw that in the bin
As her family had a party
And were hearty

All that work paid off
And it didn't cost a cough
So she joined in with the party
And her friends were crafty

Mind, she was only ten at the time
So you too can rhyme!

Amelia Pietrzak (9)

My Perfect Dream

I have a dream where the sky is always blue
Where the sea is always crystal-clear with a lovely
turquoise colour

I have this amazing dream where wild animals are
not dangerous anymore
Where children all around the world are able to
play with them without fear

I have a lovely dream where there is no place for
rubbish and pollution anymore
Where the entire earth is sparkling clean

I have a wonderful dream where all the people
from different countries, nations and tribes
Are living happily together like a big united family
Where there is no room for hatred, partiality,
cruelty or sufferings

I have a big dream where money is powerless and
useless
Where everyone is able to have a nice place to live
Where there is no room for poverty and
homelessness

I have a great dream where all of us are helping
one another
To cultivate the soil and to plant our own food
Where the spirit of giving and sharing is all over
the place

I have a dream in which my perfect dream
As absurd and unreal as it may sound
Has finally become a reality.

Yerielle Antoine (8)

My Seasons

Spring
Spring is what you call beautiful, calm, quiet and wonderful.
It makes you wonder how much longer, how much longer it will last,
because in the summer, green takes over and gives a warm blast!
Summer's blast is its magic source but spring has a delicate force.
Will it be enough or will it be too much?

Summer
Summer is the king, he is as bright as your ring.
He's hot, he's on fire and we like him a lot.
He is quick, he is cunning but we're always burning.
He is glad, he is gold but there is one thing he is afraid of, he is afraid of the cold.

Autumn
The sky is raining leaves and the trees...
well they are just standing still and stand there they will.
They will try, don't make fun, don't lie,

For the autumn leaves are clever so don't trust them. Never.
When it's windy they take to the skies because they do believe that they can fly.

Winter
Snow trickles down my windowpane, I snuggle up in a lion's mane.
I return home, sit near the fire, I have no idea why I called you a liar.
Winter is cold, got nowhere to go, I guess I'm a mole, because I'm digging in the snow.

Theadora Yap (9)

Wish Upon A Star

The path of night will find its way,
Engraved in bronze, silver and gold,
The path is longer than the day,
No one knows what the sky beholds.

He lies on a bed of dark blue cloth,
He sits on a curtain of dark raven,
The sky's silk can be silky or soft,
The sky can hold a fantasy cavern.

My star lets out ribbons of carmine, hazel and
amber,
He shines brighter than a sprinkle of sparkling
glitter,
When streams of light reflect off his shiny skin,
they dance the samba,
Millions of stars littered the sky, they burn away
and wither.

Night arrives, curtains drawn, the stars dance and
have a ball,
I look around, seeing them dance, I breathe in, and
begin my wish,

I wish upon a star, I draw it on my wall,
I look and stare, blow him a kiss, then I clean my
midnight dish.

You've sailed the sky as I sleep,
Then I awake to have a peek,
You've gone, you've disappeared I need another
wish,
While you were gone I ate my pet fish.
I want him back,
I'll get a slap please give me him back.

Your journey comes to an end,
Once I awake again you've turned the bend.
Goodbye my friend!

Caitlin Burton (10)

Jesus

The three wise men walked afar,
And they followed a big bright star.
They finally arrived at the stable where he lay,
Lying in a basket of straw and hay.

Baby Jesus,
He never cries.
Baby Jesus,
In a feeding box, he lies.

When you call his name,
He'll come straight away.
If he ever went to school,
There would be no delay.

If you put him to bed,
He would sleep like a log.
If you took him to the park,
He wouldn't mess about in a bog.

If you taught him how to write and read,
He would write and read with no mislead.

He survived in the desert for forty days,
Without any food, without any praise.

That's why you should praise the king,
Because he is nice, and because he is bling.
He doesn't turn around to talk to his mates,
Instead of writing the title and the date.

He cleansed us of our sins,
He put the sins all in a bin.
His faith is as big as a mammoth,
We need to keep Sunday the Sabbath.

Anaia Grace Steele (8)

Space Adventure

A space tiger travelling through the stars.
In a jaguar rocket ship heading to Mars.
Upon a cratered asteroid, the stripy tiger sees.
A three-headed purple alien with speckled orange knees.
Quickly turning then landing, the tiger steps out of the rocket.
Greeting the alien politely, he pulls a sock out of his pocket.
Handing the sock over the tiger respectfully says
"This will keep your head warm on cold days."
With a grin and a blurb, he puts on the spotty sock.
Waves goodbye graciously and jumps off the space rock.
Then like a volcanic eruption, tiger's rocket takes flight.
With flames burning behind it, it shoots tiger through the night.
But oh no! Oh dear! A space monster attack.
It's going to turn tiger's rocket into a super space snack!
With a munch and a crunch, the monster takes a bite.

But it was only a dream, the house cat wakes with a fright.
Waking safely in his basket with a saucer of cream.
No more space adventures this house cat would dream.

Sara Coulter (8)

My Trip To The Milky Way

I can see the bright shimmering stars in the night
sky
I can see the glittery rainbow-coloured swirling
Milky Way
I can hear the warm crackling of the sun
The fire loudly bursts out of the great big ball
Of boiling gasses and makes a big splash
I can touch the rocky hard grey mountains of
Mercury
I can feel the cloudy cotton atmosphere of Venus
I can sit on the red rusty rocks of Mars
I can experience the rainy storms of the red spot
on Jupiter
I can run around the sparkly faint icy rings of
Saturn
I can nudge into place the slanted cold Uranus
I might get trapped in the whirling winds of
Neptune
I can taste the brown, rough, hard rocky dust from
the big gigantic bumpy asteroid that floats around
gently

I can smell the smoky red-hot fire shooting out of
the giant rocket
The fire is as hot as an oven
I touch the melting glassy window you can see
Earth from
I feel the cloudy soft atmosphere of Earth, take a
deep breath
Then with a little bump I land back on Earth.

Yumie Palliyage (8)

Four Seasons

Crisp golden leaves whirl around in the brisk
autumn breeze,
Making most of the outdoors and climbing trees,
Nervousness of meeting new teachers and
classmates,
Wonderstruck with the sparkly skies, that the
Fireworks set ablaze.

Christmas is round the corner, don't fight over the
mistletoe
At least I have the nativity play, so let's put on a
show!
Last night I dreamt of snow, but it's only wet and
cold
Getting ready to bring in the new year, goodbye to
the old!

Start of spring, it is no longer dark when I go to
school,
Colours coming back, it's raining cherries, the
berries looking cool,
Cricket club is here, let's score some sixes and
fours!
Easter bunny I love you, but I love the Kinder egg a
little more!

Summer's here, let's play without a care,
Fresh breeze and rising hot air,
Sun is shining with its blazing golden beam,
Ding ding here comes the ice cream!

I love the four seasons, autumn, winter, summer, spring,
I like that they are different, love the variety that they bring!

Yashmeet Singh

Aliens I Know

There was an alien named Sparvobot
Who lived on Planet Mar
Sparvobot liked to play with Marotot
But could not drive a car!

There was an alien named Doomite
Who lived on Planet Ramacharge
Doomite liked to give Dino a fright
Who got his revenge with Barge!

There was an alien named Gladiapix
Who lived on Planet Return
Gladiapix really like to get things to fix
And his most liked food was fern.

There was an alien named Hypa-zite
who lived on planet Steel
Hypa-zite, who was really fond of zucchinite
would not eat any veal!

There was an alien named Gladace
who lived on planet Spirulos

he loved to eat space-a-los virace
and he beat every single boss!

There was an alien named Sparkevour
who lived on planet Taser
spi-virus was what he liked to devour
with a hint of fresh lase!.

There aren't more aliens I know
This is the end so let's go.

Rushaananth Srirankan (10)

When The World Changes

The sea levels rise
The ice melts
Was it wise
All those years no one helped?

The planet is polluted
Nature dying down
Because of human's carelessness
Everything is changing round.

The jungle used to dance and thrive
It had a party every night
But now there is a loneliness
And never sings or jives.

The Arctic adventure
Every footstep
Reveals a new surprise
But now the ice is melting
And all the excitement has died.

Once cared flowers and trees
All rotten, slowly die away
Mother Nature calls SOS
The planet has turned a mess
But greedy people turn around
They walk away and keep their ground.

Derelict, destroyed
Endless and empty
Overfished oceans
There are plenty.

But don't stay down in the doom and gloom
There is something that you could do
Think of the positive
Make a change
Have your voice heard and be brave!

Anna Stavroula Goebel (11)

The Alien At The Door

Slimy gloop
Eerie sound
Shake from my head to the ground.

Odd smell
State of shock
Lifts his wet tentacle and knocks.

Scared stiff
Courage flown
Creeping downstairs all alone.

Takes key
Opens door
Waves the creature along the floor.

Small fists
Sticky hands
Closes door and shakes his hand.

Chewing tongue
Pleads for help
His planet being ruled by Zelts!

Shocked face
Biting lip
Follows him to the spaceship.

Shuts door
Fires up
Dome has zero guts.

Flips switch
Starts to rise
I am in for a surprise.

Land on Mars
See the Zelts
I look up and call for help.

Get my squash
Spray them all
Makes them laugh to the floor.

Pick up one
Throw him up
others watch, startled and hushed.

They retreat
Victory!
Shake hands with my new friend... Lee!

Raghav Singla (8)

As Dreams

I woke up in a world where humans had wings, wings like an angel's with snow-white feathers. Rivers were rainbow and golden leaves were on the trees, swaying in the soft breeze. I found I could fly but then I met a thing, a cloud of gold surrounding it.

It said it was a protector of the Earth, the ozone layer and wildlife was heard, they had feelings too and not just us. They had a voice and a great power.

The creature turned out to be a legendary Goldragon Keeper, two of them left in the whole universe. This creation I was in was a world of fantasy they wanted to live in. It was perfect and everyone was jolly and no games or consoles or vehicles were in sight. I smiled and suddenly was blinded by a flash, beams were all around me, and woke up in my room.

But I looked onto my desk. A crisp, white, heavenly feather glistened on it. How... how did it get here?

Natalia Tyl (10)

Aliens

Slimy and green,
They've been seen,
Never turn round,
Or you might hear a sound!

They live on the moon and wake when noon,
Never look, never stare, never look anywhere.
They'll come after you, so watch out you
astronauts.

Will you hide or stay outside, I don't know,
Which would you dare, maybe hide in your hair?
Maybe hide under there, hide with the moon stars
or their crew!
Take a peek, maybe a sneak, maybe the vegetable
that's called a leek.

What else is there to explore, maybe other planets
can't we.
Let's see which planet might we be on,
Will it be Mars? If it is, let's grab a few Mars bars!
Take the spacecraft and eat in there.
Can't there be a few pears, can't there be a few
lairs,

Can't there be a few chairs, why not?
Is it hot and no air?
Or is it the snot that lies under there?

Watch out for slime that might be them!

Suri Rogers

Swamp Tigers And Mainly Climbing Hedgehogs

Last night I watched a video,
Well maybe two or three,
One was about a tiger, that was very hungry,
That night I learnt something very new, that
swamp tigers dooo exist!
And I'll add something else too,
Now, I know you may be thinking that EVERYONE
knows a hedgehog,
But I don't think you knew...
They have razor nails on their cute climbing feet,
And they climb up trees with a super singing beat,
Now I know you think I'm joking, but it's true, I
swear,
The only thing I'm lying about is the singing beat, I
will share,
And if you still don't believe me then ask me all the
questions you want,
But I won't worry because I'll answer them like tic
tac tump,

Another thing you probably think is silly,
Is that I'm writing about a carnivore and a cute,
climbing omnivore,
Well I think they go quite well together,
Just like a fruit and a beautiful, white feather!

Abigail Hollamby (9)

My Love For Reading

My love for reading is astronomical
I really can't stop
I read every day
With my favourite place being a bookshop
My love for reading
Some people think I'm different
But of course, I don't listen
Reading takes me on journeys
And expeditions
My love for reading
Reading improves my knowledge
And makes me ready my ambitions
With my biggest one being a lawyer in the future
Reading puts me in a high position
My love for reading
I love reading new stories
And writing them too
It makes happier
And I love spreading this feeling through
My love for reading
Reading makes me, me

It alters me
It makes me stand out from the crowd
And makes me feel free
My love for reading
Reading makes me, me
It makes me amazing
And those facts I deeply agree
In this world, surely, it makes an impact
My love for reading shall never die.

Mistura Adebambo (11)

Our Planet's Paradise

Someone's creeping,
Along the forest floor,
A leopard leaps out,
And gives a roar.

The exotic understorey,
Flooding with life,
Only we can save it,
On the edge of a knife.

Kings of the canopy,
Soaring up high,
The dazzling birds,
Painting the sky.

The emergent trees,
It took them centuries to grow,
No one has the right,
To make them go.

The animals who live there,
Can't live there anymore,

Their precious homes,
Sadly burned to the floor.

This heavenly paradise,
'The lungs of the world,'
But something's not right,
It's all muddled and twirled.

It is our duty to save,
This beautiful place,
Put an end to the fires,
It's having to face.

This is a message,
From the trees,
Save our rainforest,
We beg you, please.

Nicole Schools (9)

Peace, The Greatest Of All Feelings

Peace improves your life,
It makes sure people don't hurt each other with a knife.
If you play with brothers and sisters you might get peace
Which is something you should do.
Putting rubbish in the bins,
Sharing a smile or maybe two!
Let's stop racism as well.
Let's try to stop being mean like pushing people in the well.
Being thankful for what you have,
Your food, shelter, family and toys.
Think about poverty,
Those unfortunate girls and boys.
Celebrating differences
Friends of different beliefs hanging out together.
Being generous forever,
Respecting your father and mother.
What a remarkable time will life become if we all were peaceful to all.

We are here to support each other and stand together so we won't fall behind.
Being calm and optimistic.
And being grateful for soldiers who died in wars.
Accepting apologies and being kind,
Let's hope people don't be cruel, giving somebody peace of mind.

Navtej Vetsa (10)

Out Of This World

Most boys would write about aliens...
But I need to get this off my chest.

Why do you say?

Do this, do that
Come on
Hurry up
Be quiet
Stop talking
You're giving me a headache...

Why did you do that?
You can do better
I've explained it a billion times
What's wrong with you?
Do you have scrambled eggs between your ears?

Your eyes will go square
That's so unhealthy
Eat bananas
Eat eggs

No screens at the dinner table
Turn it off... now!

Don't you ever ever ever lie
Don't be physical
Use your words
Don't be rude
Don't answer back
Don't tease

Focus focus *focus*
Are you blind?

Stop being a baby
You're not old enough...
Grow up!

Stop daydreaming?
Sit still
Stay on your chair
Come on... move
Don't push the boundaries
I'm not going to do it for you
How many times have I told you...

I'm only eight but all I want to be is:

Out of this World...

Ishan Datta (8)

Out Of The Earth

Do you ever wonder what's going on in space?
Sharks and rhinos could be hit with cake on the face.
The aliens could be eating talons of ice cream
Or pushing each other in the queue for food whilst having a dream.

Do you ever think about what is happening in a star's mind?
They could be finding cheese or making a hippopotamus and aliens combine.
Because of them, all the flamingos are out of control,
Or they might be begging to have snow like bubblegum from moon trolls.

Do you ever think about what aliens do when they see the moon?
They pack their bags with hot dogs and food,
They put on their swimsuits and dive into the solar system sky.
They think they are extraordinary, but really they don't know how to fly.

Haseena Sophia Hamdard (11)

The Mysterious Blob

What's that in space?
It looks like a mace.
Except blackish red,
With an egg for a head.

Oh look it's changing,
Maybe it's from Beijing!
We must move with haste,
If we don't want to stop the human race!

"Call the space team!"
They're in a small bean!
That's no use,
Call Mrs Moose.

She stops the blob,
But loses track of it.
Okay we'll use a Fit Bit,
We find the blob.

But as we reach it,
It goes back to space,
"Goodbye human race!"

In the nick of time,
The blob turns into slime.
It now runs away.
At least we saved the day!

As we were celebrating,
The blob was busy creating...
We found a hog,
Inside a bog,
It was the blob!

But it didn't notice us,
So we drove on it with a bus,
That was the end of the blob.
"Bye-bye blob!"

Tofunmi Joel (9)

Russia

Russia is a different world, out of this world,
As the plane flies in low
The city is blanketed in snow
Shrouded in a sheet of white
Simply the most magical sight
Little white elves fall from the sky
Giant figures down below
Layered up tight against the snow.
The countryside is wide and vast
As it was in days gone past
The wind is sailing through the clouds
The land is free from madding crowds.
With my cousins all together
We are all best friends forever
Little sleep and lots to say
We talk and laugh, whisper and play.
Lots of room but never apart
My family fill up my heart.
When we leave the cosy home
Through the snow hills we go roam
Our snowball fights are endless fun

We leap and dash, hide and run.
My dad joins in, transformed to a child
Excited as us and just as wild
Russia is my world.

Milana Kim

If I Was In Charge

If I was in charge of the world I would ban cabbage!
The green stuff, the vegetables they are all garbage!
Bedtime at ten, and sweets all day!
Not listening to our parents (we do that anyway!)

No more wars, no more fights!
I will make sure that everything would be alright!
No more knives, no more guns!
I'll make sure that there are no more hit-and-runs!

No more unfair treatment towards different people!
I'll make sure there are no more people that are evil!
No more persecutors, no more tormentors!
I'll make sure nobody is saying "I resent her!"

No more people being ashamed of who they are!
Being depressed because they don't have the latest car!

No more people afraid to be themselves!
I'll make sure everyone is able to excel!

If I was in charge of the world
I would make sure everyone is loved!
No more sorrow, no more sadness just plain old
love!

Guisepina Soremi (11)

My Cat Misty

Misty is my beautiful, fluffy, thick, furry, grey cat,
From his ears to his tail the fur covers like a
shaggy mat,
He curls up in his bed at night like a cute, little ball,
Sometimes so small and tight I can't even see his
eyes at all.

He gallops, pounces and runs after a delicious
treat,
He is so happy playing his tail stands up like a
curly piece of wheat,
He claims my lap as a place to sit what a cheeky
little pickle,
The purrs are so loud when you give him a chin
tickle.

He sits at our table waiting for some food or drink,
Milk is his favourite I definitely think,
At night he is noisy and meows really loud,
It gives me a fright which seems to make him
proud.

His emerald, twinkling eyes always shimmer,
Waiting at the window for our car to glimmer,

We are greeted by his meows and he weaves round and round.
Misty is so much happier, when we are at home and around.

Amber Martin (11)

No Name

The woman that dances upon the wind
The woman who fixes things that cannot be fixed
She is the girl with no name
Her feelings are all mixed.

Flooding, droughts and heatwaves are above her
powers
Forests dying, animals are extinct
Nobody sees the pain
Because everyone has blinked.

No Name feels the sorrow
Having no home is her speciality
We can change our ways
But no one has immortality.

Co2 pollutes the air
We never really notice
Breathing on
It's not our main focus.

No Name isn't the only one
Helpers have no name

Conservationists have no name
But big businesses have control of the game.

Watching their power strengthen
The list of fought lengthens.

Who is No Name
Mother Nature is the one who became.

Katie Lynn-Jones (11)

The Sweet Scent Of Spring

Winter is cold and covered in fear
Whilst spring is joyful and full of cheer
And now the time is finally here
Where winter turns to spring at this time of year...

Elegant flowers begin to grow
As the sapphire sky beams aglow
While dazing daffodils begin to stun
Lazy lilies bathe in the sizzling sun.

In the corner of my eye
Bees take off and begin to fly
Ants start marching from underground
Forging ahead without a sound.

Migrated birds are now where they belong
Merrily singing their favourite songs.
Bears wake up from their colossal dens
Ready to hunt with their fearless friends!

The sweet scent of spring fills the air
With happiness and excitement to share
As the flowers bloom, as the birds soar
There's a whole new world that I'm waiting for!

Diya Sapkota (9)

My Cricket Dream

I have always had a dream,
To play for the England cricket team.
Hitting the ball with all my might
Practising both day and night.

Looking smart all dressed in white,
Hoping the umpire has good eyesight.
Listening to the cheering crowd
Getting excited, shouting loud.

Something I find lots of fun,
Is when I score lots of runs.
However, my favourite part of cricket,
Is helping the team to take a wicket.

If I played for England I would,
Travel the world when I could.
Using a train, a plane or bus
Taking wickets without a fuss.

Making sure I catch the ball,
Hoping I don't trip or fall.

Waiting to hear the umpire call "Out"
Is what cricket is all about.

So while I sit and watch TV,
I dream that one day it will be me
Lifting the Ashes trophy over my head,
The sound of my name filling the Aussies with dread.

Kamran Patel (8)

The Haunted House

I don't know where I am,
Who hit me on my eye?
I know it's a creepy house
Wait! Is that a mouse?
I'm scared of mice
Or is it headlice?
Bats are coming down
Is this a vampire town?
I can see a scary ghost
Who is carrying a mysterious post
I'm getting freaked out
Shall I think about people that shout?
I'll be brave and give a wave
But monsters can lock me in a cave.
I have to ask them, "Are you real?"
I think that my stupid brain had a deal
I want to leave this house before I see a mouse,
Oh this is bad
The monsters are not glad
They are licking their lips
To eat me with chips

I'm trying to run away
When I heard my friend say
"Wake up Kareem,
It is just a silly dream."

Jodi Badewi (8)

Outer Space

Ground control off we go,
As we count down from ten.
Leaving the Earth far below,
In the footsteps of mighty men.

As we reach the moon,
Floating amongst the stars.
Shooting towards Neptune,
Whizzing past Mars.

Mercury is miles behind,
Like the boiling Venus.
It's cold here, but we don't mind,
As we travel past Uranus.

Fly, you flame-tailed rocket,
Far from the distant sun.
Zooming like a comet,
Towards Cygnus X-1.

Blinking now a small green dot,
Our precious home the Earth.

It's the only one we've got,
In this vast universe.

Turning towards Taurus,
We conclude our adventure in space.
We sing a joyful chorus,
As we return to the human race.

Charlie Durling (8)

Chorus

Space is a never-ending space,
Every minute every second it is growing.
Every star is far a-part,
Millions and zillions of them there are.
You know there's something orbiting Earth,
It is the fascinating moon!

Let's talk about the moon,
The fascinating moon.
The moon is part of Earth,
Made from Earth's stone.
When a meteorite crashes Earth,
Rocks go flying making the moon.

How are stars made,
Let's look at ours first.
Stars being as clouds of gas,
The cloud gets thicker the gas gets hotter.
Other stars get bigger until they explode,
This is called a supernova.

Time for the glittering galaxies,
The solar system is one galaxy.

In the middle of most galaxies there are,
Giant red stars they are the oldest stars in the
galaxy.
Old stars die in galaxies,
And new ones form to.

Charles Zhou (8)

Planet Toe

A boy called Joe had a very sore toe,
He looked up at the sky,
It was so very very high,
He built a toe-shaped rocket,
Climbed in and said "Goodbye!"
Whoosh... the toe-shaped rocket fired deep into space,
One year later, the toe-shaped rocket landed on a planet far far away.

Imagine Joe's surprise, the planet was filled with Toe Aliens.
Big toes, small toes, middle toes, all types of toes speaking toe language.
All of a sudden Joe's toe felt better,
They decided to celebrate,
By writing a letter,
To welcome the toe better.

Joe's toe decided to stay on the welcoming Planet Toe,
This was a problem for poor old Joe because he just wanted to go!

Sebastian Markson (8)

Love

So, what is love? Is it just two genders crushing on each other?
So listen to what happened to me, because it was like
Every smile towards one another
Every talk or game
It was like every memory was rubbed off with sun eraser
Along with my shattered heart
We were never a real thing
But I like to imagine
I once called you my 'the kind one'
You used me and threw me out like garbage
I guess this is it, my love
The end of our journey
That was almost discovered to be real
Or was it?
I guess I could never ask you
I would imagine us on our first date in Enfield town
Holding each other's hands nervously
But now that I think about it,
You were never really there.

Bintou Sillah (13)

Typical Weather

It's already January,
And I am complaining,
That it hasn't snowed yet this winter,
It's only been raining,
Bucket fulls,
Wheelbarrow fulls,
Of soaking wet rain,
But not a single snowflake,
With its delicacy and intricate patterns.
How I long
To catch one on my tongue
And feel its beauty melt away.
I will keep hoping!

It's already April,
And I am complaining (again),
That the sun hasn't shone yet this spring,
It's only been snowing.
Snow's way too cold for me:
It freezes my tongue,
And now we're snowed in.
Where's the sunshine?

It'll brighten up the days,
With its rays of warmth showering us.
I just can't wait,
For the days to get longer
And for the snow to melt away.
Let's be patient,
Again!

Ayla Chard (11)

The Fearless Friendship Four

The Fearless Friendship Four are superheroes in outer space
Saving people, planet to planet they race
On Mars is their base
On their vehicle named ace
They all have an unbelievable pace
If you are lucky, with them you could come face to face.

The Fearless Friendship Four love their work
Around every corner you will find them lurk
If you call any one of them a jerk
They'll simply just give you a smirk
They keep everything in order so nothing goes beserk.

The Fearless Friendship Four never get tired of beating the bad guys
They always keep their eyes on the prize
And so they rise

Following the cries
And you won't believe it, but they love fries.

Mariam Asgher (10)

Stay Positive

If you are ever feeling blue
Find something you like to do
Sing out loud for all to hear
That might help to spread some cheer

If you are ever feeling sad
Think about good times you've had
Hopefully they will make you smile
And make you happy for a while

If you are ever feeling down
Do your best not to frown
Take a bath or a shower
Have a nap for half an hour

If you are ever feeling teary
And noticed you are feeling weary
Try some exercise or a hobby
Maybe even walk your doggy

If you are ever feeling low
Like you have nowhere to go

Just know I'll always be your friend
We will stick together until the end.

James Mannion (8)

Wrong Turn

I think I must've taken a wrong turn
Because my stomach begins to churn
It is late at night in the wood
Behind me I see a figure in a hood
Then I hear their eerie voice
Do I listen and make that choice?
It whispers quietly in my ear
"Help me and get me out of here!"
I begin to run as fast as I can
Nowhere to go and no plan
All of the trees look the same
Is this a dream or video game?
All it does is follow me
Now I really have to flee
Suddenly I see some light
I run to it, still full of fright
To my relief I find a river
I climb into a boat, I must not dither
I row and row, my fingers cold, in pain
I will never ever return again.

Rosanna Luca (10)

As

Flying through space and time
What comes to be when the light has gone past its prime?
Through the intergalactic interstate, will the interlopers sense the malevolence?
What comes about when the light has gone to infinity and beyond?
Will the hidden species of the galaxy gasp upon detecting that the glowing ball has gone?
What comes to pass when the light does not spread far and wide?
Does the lingering essence of the malevolent diminish all hope?
Who will defeat this being when the light has gone and darkness surrounds?
Can the rightful saviour bring the lightness into the void of desolation?
Who will protect the ocean of emptiness from its infinite doom?
You...

Tayyabah Butt (11)

What Is Space?

What is space?
A vast, cosmic abyss,
Or a palace full of secrets
That we always miss?

Space is everywhere,
It's a blanket for the universe.
It's in your house and car
And even in your purse!

Space is a monster,
It swallows everything in its path.
It gives you nightmares of darkness,
So you can feel its wrath.

Space is a mystery,
It's full of things that are anonymous.
It has a boxful of secrets at its disposal,
That still remain to us mysterious.

Space is endless
It's bigger than we'll ever be.

It stretches thousands of light-years from end to
end
That we'll never be able to see.

Taha Shahid (10)

Flip It

Bullying is a threat,
Social, cyber, physical,
It can happen with people you've just met;
These people are typical.

Let's start off with social,
Spreading, excluding and abusing;
This goes up to another level,
Stop all this commanding.

Next up cyber,
Facebook, Insta and Roblox,
Why do 'friends' have to be liars;
Stop all these mocks!

Finally physical,
Stealing, tripping, hitting;
This act is very critical,
Think about the opposite feeling!

Our planet is a very beautiful place,
It is our responsibility to keep it spinning;

Though we need a little more grace,
Lets put an end to bullying.

Hannah Farida Bhatti (10)

Stars

Have you ever wondered
Why stars twinkle in the sky?
Would you even bother?
Would you even try?

It is by the deteriorations in our atmosphere
And by which direction the wind is found
And so that is why
We see them twinkle from the ground.

Don't they look so beautiful?
Just lying down on your blanket and staring at the
sky
When the weather is perfectly fine
Not too rainy nor too dry.

Did you see a shooting star?
Remember to make a wish!
Did you wish for no laundry?
Or the fisherman for once catches the fish?

All you do
Is stare into space

Hey I made a punchline
Just look at your laughing face!

Tansi Jakhar (10)

Life In Minecraft

I get up in the morning and mine some wood
To make tables and swords, they'd better be good

For lunch, soup is my favourite dish
Certainly better than a stinky fish

I've been digging around for diamonds and gold
And when I've got plenty they all can be sold

I use a hoe to plant lots of seeds
When the garden gets messy I get rid of all of the weeds

Zombies are the easiest to fight
While they wander about all through the night

I've built tall buildings and roller-coaster rides
But when the Ender dragon come everyone hides

I like to play Minecraft night and day
In my village is where I stay.

Tyler Young (8)

Water, Water, Water

People, people, people why are you so cruel?
I saw you do this or that
It's all you do

Water splashing in my hands
I wonder how you feel
People are careless and using you
By putting dirt and waste into you

Are you happy about what you did?
Well I hope not
Because what you have done was mean.

I remember the day when I was swimming in the
ocean
And saw the plastic next to me
I felt sad for you so I took the plastic out
And decided to make you laugh.

Water, water, water,
Sorry for what people have done to you
I wish people would care more
And help you and look after the environment.

Bella Bee (9)

Peace To Me

Peace to me is a bubble bath,
I also like to have a laugh.

Peace to me is chilling with Iyla,
Together our friendship name is Tyla.

Peace to me is dancing to Anne Marie,
I like to dance as me.

Peace to me is a clear mind,
Positivity is what you need to find.

Peace to me is kindness and kindness to care,
Our world is just and nice and fair.

Peace to me is a warm cup of tea,
I like to put my feet in the sea.

Peace to me is shopping at lush,
I also love a raspberry slush.

Peace to me is watching a movie,
I also enjoy a day with bouji.

Peace to me is a smile on everyone's face,
My aunt's house is my happy place.

Peace to me is being the first me,
And not trying to be the second nobody.

Tia Aymer (11)

A Trip To Sweden

I went to Sweden for four days,
and travelled in many ways.
Arlanda Express and on a train,
tube, metro and also a plane.

The Vasa Museum, you must go and see,
I went there with my family.
But after counting one, two, three,
Vasa sank into the Baltic Sea.

Sheraton Hotel was a lovely stay,
but there wasn't enough space to play.
Although the room was small,
I ended up at Stockholm Mall.

Gamla Stan, the city's old town,
where many tourists wander around.
Colourful buildings, cobbled lanes,
but then, it was time for the aeroplane.

This holiday has been really great,
but now I'm longing for another break.

Goodbye Sweden I must say,
but I'll be back another day.

Hayden Lam (9)

The Day The Humans Went To Space

The day the humans set off to space
They came across an unordinary place
The place was filled with aliens
Who all had faces of demons

It was great until they were spotted in the sky
With flashing lights passing by
It was almost like the world had been flipped,
And they themselves had been roughly kicked.

It was almost like their eyes had been closed
The demon-like aliens had been exposed
They still haunt us day by day
Even when you're in your Chevrolet

What do they really have to say?
Or have they just come to play?
To this day we don't really know
Why don't we just wave hello?

Lola Stokes (11)

Respect Our Planet

Fish and sea creatures swim into bottles and can't get out
They wiggle and waggle oh my, how they shout
No one can hear them, oh no they can't get out.

Animals are getting killed
They won't trust us any more

Some people are mean
To animals they have seen
When you look, it will seem as if you are blind
The animals you once saw, you now will no longer find

No pets to hold
No animals to see
Some get sold
Caution, the human holds the key

You are burning their hearts
You are tearing them apart
What oh what are they going to do
Their forests are burning and so might you.

Amelia-Jane Charleton

Dogs

I saw a dog today and it smiled at me
Then it started chasing me
So I hid behind a tree

Up the tree I went
All my time was spent
I sent the dog to kent

Stuck up the tree I was
Scream for help because
Some bees began to buzz

Fuzzy black and yellow
We meet again old fellow
"Go away" I began to bellow

Above me was a beehive
I jumped to stay alive
A car started to drive

Dogs are my allergy
They take up all my energy
They're secretly my frenemy

So where could I hide?
As another dog walked with pride
I ran back home, I tried.

Subha Jarin

Devastating Life

Going to school with bad thoughts,
My friends and I are all nerds,
With trouble on my side, I feel weak,
Telling the teacher will be such a relief,

With people on me, I'm so outnumbered,
To see the changes is such a bummer,
All day, all night, I am very worried,
Shaking and shivering will build up confidence,

I confront the principle with my say,
To show the crowd he won't delay,
Pumping and pounding my heart put my sorrows
to shame,
Showing those haters I got no one to blame,

Living out of this world,
It may be hard,
It may be difficult,
But you just have to deal with it,

Temiloluwa Emmanuel Kalejaiye (10)

Today

It all started with one creative mind
Somebody who wanted to put the past behind
To start a new future and show the world what
they've got
Surely it would take an inventor or genius,
someone with a lot
Someone who wanted a bright future that they
wouldn't be there to see
A happy fun place just for you and me
A person who was ready to believe
That every time you try hard you get closer to
achieve
Something that is greater than words can explain
Something's special for a person with a big brain
The world gets smarter and more intelligent every
day
A person like this is why we live in a fantastic world
today.

Anne-Marie Mensah (11)

Beautiful Animals

In this world,
There are so many people.
It's way over the amount of big gold rings.
I like people,
But I think some are bit too greedy,
Including me.
It's the animals that are needy.
Animals are my friends.
I want them to be free.
I wonder and ponder,
As they ask me...
"Maple, what did we do to be treated like this?
Are we mean? Do we take up too much space?
Is it we are too loud or stinky?
Or are we a waste?"
And I respond, "No, my dear companion,
It is not you that is trouble
It is we humans that are mean and
The greedy people make you uncomfortable."
So let's be kinder,
Let's make friends.

Eat vegetables,
And do amend.

Maple MacGloin (10)

Out Of This World

It's an amazing experience
The wonderful sights
Lots of rocks and dust
Good view of the stars

Terrible asteroids surrounding Earth
It might hit our planet
The satellite orbits the world
Can we see the aliens?

The sun gives light and warmth
Moon reflects light on Earth
All planets orbiting the sun

Beautiful shooting stars
Wonderful and unique shapes
No gravity and air in space
It's scary over there

The universe includes billions of them
Even stranger stars there are
Scientists are still facing new inventions
All this happening in the universe.

Dathusan Thavaneswaran (10)

I Swis Like Ziss

I swis like ziss, I swis like ziss,
The ways of the wind and sea.
I swis like ziss, I swiz like ziss,
Together you and me.

The lion's den, dark and dank,
Bones litter the floor like a carpet of death.
The hyena of theft has cubs as a snack,
That's not where I want to be.

A new litter of cubs you'll see on the ground,
Waiting for mum to bring lunch.
They may look cute
But do not touch,
They have sharp teeth as you'll come to see.

I swis like ziss, I swis like ziss,
The ways of the wind and sea.
I swis like ziss, I swiz like ziss,
Together you and me.

Ella Hargreaves (8)

Area 51

Out of this world is the life in space
Where no one there is in the human race
People like to think that way up there
Aliens are flying in spaceships somewhere
Area 51 tells us nothin'
Apart from it's where aliens might be livin'
It's protected by a gazillion guards
Even for me to get in there it's really hard
So please don't go to Area 51
Or even to get famous - you won't be number one
It's a silly thing to do I daresay
A waste of your time and a waste of your day
You don't want it to be your last day ever...
So go to Area 51 never!

Isabel Barefield (11)

Llamas

Llamas, llamas rolling on the floor,
Another llama chewing on someone's door,
Llamas, llamas jumping on the table,
Another llama sleeping inside a cradle,
Llamas, llamas running out of breath,
Another llama starts working as a chef,
Llamas, llamas watching as time goes by,
Another llama forgot to say goodbye,
Llamas, llamas running so fast,
Another llama realised their curfew they had passed,
Llamas, llamas time to go home,
Another llama stands on their own,
Llamas, llamas need a break,
For they are all starting to ache,
Dancing around was a big mistake.

Megan Lee (9)

Stars

We twinkle brightly in the night,
So to watch us just sit tight.
We fly through the everlasting sky,
Over Vancouver, over Shanghai.

Big bang and clustered high,
Boom! Then scattered like moondust in the sky.
At the start we were with all our friends,
Now the blackness around us never ends.

Flashing and flickering, we burn through all our shells,
Bright lights but we let off no smells.
Orange, blue, white, yellow or red,
The silky, black sky is our bed.

Restless at night, we creep into your thoughts
Gleaming and glittering, seen up close by astronauts.
We twinkle brightly in the night,
So to watch us just sit tight!

Joseph Lyons (10)

Wonderful Wildlife

I see the hares hopping and the squirrels searching
on the muddy forest floor
I see the swans swimming and the seagulls
stealing at the sandy coast
I see the tigers tracking and the snakes sleeping in
the damp jungle
I see the lions leaping and the gazelles grazing in
the sunny savannah
I see the leopards leaping and the owls observing
on the frosty mountaintop
I see the rays racing and the fish flying in the
bubbling ocean
I see the butterflies blooming and the ladybirds
lulling in the melodic meadow
I see the hawks hunting and the falcons fluttering
at the isolated cliffs
I hear the lean lynxes lullabying me off to sleep...

Isabelle May Wooldridge (10)

Lost In The Darkness

Lost in the darkness was young Chase,
Flying above the endless void.
He was floating in space,
Wanting his friend Floyd.

In the ship was Chase's friend Floyd,
Scared for Chase's life.
The man was feeling very annoyed,
As he thought about Chase day and night.

They had been friends for life,
But now that had ended.
Chase and Floyd started to cry,
As the tears made the panels busted.

Floyd forgot about his friend
And fixed the ship.
He set off to descend
Back to Earth with a zip.

Lost in the darkness was young Chase,
Flying above the endless void.

He was floating in space,
He had no one, not even Floyd.

Harrison Darwin (10)

Six Ways To Look At The Moon

Moon, you are like a sun without flames,
Swimming through the endless seas of space,
Trying to escape the darkness.

Be yourself moon!
Do not fade away into the shadows.

Moon, how do you feel waiting
In the empty seaside of darkness lost where no
one visits?

I know your only wish moon,
Is to have a brother so when the sun turns its back
on you,
You'll have someone to talk to.
Moon, you can run through the night sky and
discover the secrets of the earth.

Open your eyes moon and admire the wonders of
the night... enjoy yourself!

George Unwin (9)

Light Up!

The clock strikes midnight in 1, 2... 3.
A new year. A new resolution. A new reality.
As fireworks soar and light the sky,
My dazzling dreams grow wings and fly.

Friends, families and fireworks,
Full of life and energy,
Provide me with encouragement
To be the best I can be.

Forget your trials and tribulations
From the year bygone,
And keep ascending like a firework
And stay strong.

Fireworks bloom like flowers of the night.
Blue! Pink! Purple! A nation full of delight.
Boom! Pop! Crackle! Fizz!
Joy and bliss.

Akshaya Jeyaseelan (10)

The Stellar Train

Chugga chugga
Clackety clack
This way and that
Across the tracks
Past Mars
And black holes too
Defying gravity
We're into the galaxy
Chugga chugga
The stellar train's off
Burning plasma
Smooth like magma
Hurtling around the Milky Way
Like a vicious tornado swirling around
Sparkling stars and vast voids
Solitude like asteroids
Through a wormhole
Our journey is done
As quick as a click
We're at Jupiter station

Then, like a lightning bolt
The stellar train vanishes into space...

Zak Gandhi (11)

Fox Eats Prey

F aster than a rabbit, it catches prey,
O n the run, like a streak of fire,
X erox it then you will see why.

E nvy its speed, it will envy your size,
A gainst a badger it will not stand a chance.
"T ime to hunt," it will say, "time to catch prey."
S care away birds in its own special way.

P atchwork beauty makes you jealous,
R unning wild to get its dinner.
E verybody tries to see it slink by,
Y ou might have seen one, but not me, not I.

Luke Turner (8)

Space Pirate

S tar stealing bandits of the sky
P illaging and plundering the planets of space
A mbitious to conquer all universes
C unning and clever, nothing will stop them
E ver!

P urple armour reflecting the stars
I gnorant and foolish nothing will stop their frenzy of greed
R oaming the planets in search of gold, power and victims
A rrogantly evading the intergalactic police and
T ormenting the souls out of unsuspecting children
E ver heard of anything more despicable?

Dylan Jones (10)

My Pet's Life

Dad is a troublemaker,
He strokes me, but he doesn't like me
Dad takes me on trips,
And always likes to poke me!
Dad I love you!

Mum is hardworking,
She feeds me my food!
Mum is helpful,
And cuddles me too!
You're the best mum a pet could ever wish for!

Sister you're annoying,
You get on my nerves!
Sister you're so loud,
You poke me! Ow!
Sister I still love you,
I cuddle you in bed!

All of my family is there,
When I need to be fed!
All of my family is there,
When they need someone to lean on!

I love them,
I love them to the moon and back and I
Always will!

Ava Cassandra Goshei (10)

Oh Who Is This?

Oh who is this?

This is Kosei my friend eating Ritz biscuits
And me with some chalk broken in bits.

Oh who is this?

This is Kosei and me drinking green tea,
Standing in front of a fake Christmas tree.

Oh who is this?

It's me as a baby
Happily sleeping, shh, shh, shh.

Oh who is this?

It's Mum and Grandma sitting in a bar
Being mad which is a bit sad.

Oh who is this?

This is Sam, my friend
Who mends metal mansions like a builder fixes the
Shard.

Roshan Merani (10)

Shall I Compare Thee To A Lollipop

Shall I compare thee to a lollipop,
Thou art more colourful and more radiant,
Rough winds do blow when I forget the sherbet,
But then I just go and walk in the desert.

If you eat too many sweets and begin to feel sick,
Just come to me and I'll fix you in a click,
Sometimes too sweet the chewy ones,
And sometimes too hot the pepper ones.

But they immortal licks shan't fade,
which eternal snacking I forsake,
So as long as men can lick and taste.
Your lollipop likeness shall not be erased.

Anne Appiah-Sarpong (10)

Pickle The Penguin

Pickle the penguin was carefree and clumsy,
Bumbling and stumbling, always quite dreamy;
He slipped on the ice, staggered twice
and fell through a hole to the ocean.

He caught a large fish, and to his surprise
Found its plastic bag gills and beady eyes
were not very tasty and terribly wasteful,
So he swam to the land, taking a stand, asking the
world to recycle.

He joined with his friends and they gathered
together,
Listening to Pickle's warnings of changes to
weather;
Climate would change, their lives take a new path,
With melting icebergs and deeper oceans for
baths.

Imogen Little (9)

The Time Traveller

One day Amy borrowed the TARDIS, the time machine of her friend - The Doctor - to visit the Vikings.

She landed on a ship full of Vikings, who pinned her down and imprisoned her in a metal cage. They said, "If you can escape then you can be our captain." Amy fumbled in her pocket and found The Doctor's sonic screwdriver, which he had entrusted her with. She zapped the lock and escaped, impressing the Vikings who gladly accepted her as their first female captain.

Amy enjoyed many great adventures with the Vikings before returning home in the TARDIS.

Ankhan Aswani (8)

Save The Environment

Seasons of change,
Seasons of growth,
There is oxygen from plants
In every breath I take,
So I never hate the environment
Even by mistake.

Environment is more precious
Than diamond and gold,
Take care of it like your beloved
Without being told.

Stop throwing litter in the ocean,
Because it is killing the sea world
And their emotion.
Plastic, plastic, read all about it.
Let's do something quick.

The world is going to be extinct
The thought of this makes me sick.

Eliza Noor Bhatti (8)

Fifty Years Later...

Fifty years later
The Earth is plain
Neither plants nor flowers
Creatures long forgotten

Fifty years later
Humans renamed 'monsters'
Killing and destroying
Creatures in their way.

Fifty years later
Our planet, truly demolished
We are putting chemicals in the atmosphere
We've completely dismantled
Our home's in danger.

Fifty years later
Our planet is gone
Animals killed, humans extinct
We have no future
Because we thought
We were deceived.

Alexandra Slavova

Love You Forever

Out of this world
What can I do?
I love u so much,
It's out in the world.
You were there when I came in the world,
You gave your loving hand to raise me,
You played with me, fed me, and cleaned me.
Even with your painful health,
You hid it well, but it still showed,
Now you have gone,
But not left me on alone.
My mum is an image that you own,
Thank you for my mum,
Thank you for your love,
I can say it loud and proud,
I will always love you Nani,
This love is out of this World.

Shiven Bhudia (10)

How Was The World Created?

How was the world created?
Why do people not know?
Maybe an alien farted,
And the Earth came out below.

How was the world created?
An explosion through the sky?
Some say it was the big bang.
But others say that's a lie.

How was the world created?
It just doesn't make any sense!
My mind is starting to swirl
This question is so intense.

How was the world created?
Was it in God's grand plan?
Did they draw their ideas in a notebook?
Is that how the world began?

Krishan Dodhia (8)

Games

It is in my hand and I'm ready to play.
Turn the button and I'm on my way.

A world of imagination is waiting for me.
Will it be exciting? Let's wait and see.

The screen comes up, for me to start.
For me to move around, to the dancing sound.

I'm pressing button A and now it's ready.
Hurry up, let's go and let me play!

3D images move across the screen.
To escape and not be seen.

Oh no! My battery is low.
I think it's now time to go.

Andre Henri Josse (8)

Weird Stuff

Dad's riding on a dino's tooth,
Mum's eating up the photo booth!
A random cow is eating brass,
And grandad's hoovering the grass!

What weird and crazy stuff!

A man down the street sits in a bin,
While a woman wears a sock of tin!
A snail on the wall has some dynamite,
And a cat's black belt is way too tight!

What weird and wild stuff!

A mole is hugging a pink, fluffy towel,
While a centipede is on the prowl!
A giraffe is chopping things with a sword,
And a boomerang is flying round the hospital ward!

What weird and wacky stuff!

Emmett Michael Hugh Lawson (10)

Peregrine Falcon

P elting across the sky,
E yes peeled for prey,
R eeling over rabbits,
E very instinct and bravery.
G liding over trees, hills and valleys,
R acing supremely
I ntimidating and fearsome,
N ever-ending glory in the skies,
E very battle won!

F antastic at flying,
A lmost dying at every turn,
L ocked in concentration,
C onjures up fantastic speed,
O n the verge of control
N erveless courage.

William Nicolson (8)

The Magic Door

I opened the magic door and saw
The eyes of a dashing cheetah
Watching my every move

I opened the magic door and heard
The swishing sound of the candyfloss machine
That I heard at the fairground

I opened the magic door and smelt
A fresh loaf of bread in France
Waiting to be eaten in the morning

I opened the magic door and touched
The tip of the T-rex tooth
From days long gone

I opened the magic door and found
The smiling pictures
Of my loving family.

Andrew MacDonald (10)

Trinity Tigers

It's a penalty!
It's me. It's all down to me.
I'm nervous. It's scary, I'm excited. I can do this.
The walk takes forever as the ball is placed down.
As I stand in the edge of the box to take the penalty,
Memories of my beloved Lionesses flood back into my mind
"Kirby, Mead, Bright, England, Hunt on the ball."
I push my foot back like a trigger on a gun.
I shoot with every last ounce of power in my body.
I have missed...
I am devastated... but the show must go on.

Poppy Hunt (10)

Friendship

F amilies are important and so are friends

R adiant, kind and caring explains them best

I n a world you can't imagine and is definitely not pretend

E very adventure we go on there is no time to rest

N ever doubting this mind-blowing land, not once

D own in this magical land anything can happen

S lowly getting closer and friendlier

H earts pumping with delight

I n a matter of time there is a lot of trust

P ass friendship to others.

Isabella Vincent-Pink (8)

Norfolk House School

At Norfolk House School
Where the teachers are cool,
You do puzzles in reception,
Year 1 learn about fiction.
Kids play football, rugby, cricket,
Goal! Try! We got a wicket!
Mad science in years 2 and 3,
Year 3 study Viking history.
Students learn piano, guitar, violin,
The school choir singing, not a din.
Years 4 and 5 at the swimming pool
Blu-Tack often a teacher's tool,
Year 6 preparing for secondary school,
Nobody here is a fool,
This is such a great school!

Abu-Bakr Ismail (10)

My Pets

My pet giraffe doesn't like having a bath.
It makes him very sad, whilst the other animals sit and laugh.
My pet monkey thinks he's funny.
He rolls around chasing my next door's bunny.
My pet bat is very chubby and fat.
He collects lots of junk and his cave is full of tat.
My pet snake likes to bake.
His favourite dish is carrot cake.
My pet frog lives under a log.
He's extremely scared of storms and the fog.
I found my pet lizard during a sandstorm blizzard.
You wouldn't believe it, but he's really a wizard.

Troy Dennis (9)

Ginger The Cat

Ginger the cat, the fluffy cat
Sitting on dogs even on their owner
If she does that don't be mad
That's because she loves you

She plays dead but don't be fooled
That means she hates you
Ginger oh ginger how adorable you are
You're just as adorable as a hamster

What tricks can you do wow
When did you learn to walk
Now that's a good cat go upstairs
Behind the Christmas tree
And go get your present
And go to sleep, goodnight!

Jack Timis (10)

Monsters

Some are big, some are small.
Some are short and some are tall.

I was sitting in my room playing my game.
When all of a sudden he popped out to explain.
That he was hiding and was really ashamed.

He and his friend had been knicking over bins.
To scare people at night and give them a fright.

Crashed and bangs all through the silent town.
Made the people shout and frown.

He then left my room looking quite sad.
Because he had been behaving very bad.

Louis Emile Josse (11)

Dear Mr Thunder God

You made me rhyme.
I'm rhyming Rhys,
Your loving niece
Who smells like sweetest lime.
With your wife Hera,
You're quite Prince Charming.
But have you ever thought,
Of a career in farming?
With a little wooden cottage,
Red, white or blue,
You and your wife Hera,
Could have someone new.
I know who...
She has a voice you made rhyme,
And she smells of sugar-sweet lime.
Guess it I do plea,
I'll give you a clue,
This person is me!
I will recite poems,
I know them off by heart!

I might even let you,
Take part!

Alice Seaman (9)

I Vow To Thee My Country

I'm so excited to go to war
To be fighting for my country
I pack my bag and as I leave
Kiss goodbye my family

Standing proud in uniform
Comrades at my side
We're marching forth in unity
We are standing side by side

Lying in the trenches
In the dead of night
All we hear is
Bang! Bang! Bang!
All day long and night.

Lying lonely on my own
The blood began to pour
As I slowly fade away
This is the truth of war.

Dolly Parsons (11)

Javier's Poem

UFOs flying through space
As if they want to have a race
Black holes at the centre of a galaxy
Which will turn astronauts into spaghetti

The illuminating stars
Are bigger than Mars
People walking on the moon
There's a chance they'll meet their doom

Venus will incinerate you
And make you sticky like glue
Since Pluto isn't a planet
It will look like a nugget

Shooting stars soar through the sky
Wishing upon them is not a lie.

Javier J Cabrera (9)

Alan The Alien

Alan the alien liked to swim,
He lived on a spaceship with his best friend Kim,
The lights on the spaceship were comfortingly dim,
I bet you've never met him!

His favourite place to land was Mars,
Where he often looked up to the stars,
And when he came down to the moon,
He narrowly avoided meeting his doom!

He next flew to Jupiter,
To watch boys and girls get stupider,
He then whizzed away to Venus,
Where he went to a school to become a genius!

Katherine Serrano (11)

So Far So Close

I watch the moon shine so very very bright
When the sunshine is no longer in sight
You make stars twinkle with all their might
Whilst there's darkness all around me left and right
At night I see angels and sometimes monsters
In my dreams I think they are both amonst us
Every day the years and seasons seem longer and
longer
Yet my memories of you remain ever so stronger
From you this planet feels light-years away
Mummy
In my heart I believe I will meet you again one day!

Hope Morton

My Bedroom

I enter my room full of joy
The curtains twist and turn
I sit down at my desk to learn
But I am tired and feel worn down
Even though I was wired to keep going
So, I turn on the TV
It opens its eyes and is brought to life
My windows blink
Then I go to my bathroom sink
I open the tap
And the water spurts out sounding *rap rap rap*
I turn the lights off and I think to myself
Thank god there's no one here
I haven't even spruced up the room!

Gibran Karim Khan (11)

Why I Want To Cook My Big Brother...

A recipe for how to cook my brother
It's a secret from my mother
Pull his teeth first
Peel the skin off
One eyeball pops
The other bursts
Shave his hair
Then you won't cough
Here the nose goes chop
The ears we share
Roast his thighs
The arms you fry
Chubby cheeks in oil
Boil, boil, boil!
Brother, brother, this is a warning
If you keep being horrid and mean
Then I will be very keen
To give you this hot bubbling bath!

Hannah Ismail (6)

High In The Sky

Planets are in outer space
Lunar is in a perfect place
Asteroids racing through the sky
Neptune wishing it could fly.

Perfect planets in the sky
I gaze upon them
As I drive by
Oh so high, oh so high.

Eight planets in total
Maybe one day
I can orbit to the stars
I particularly like majestic Mars.

Majestic Mars, the overlooker of stars
Red, rocky, bumpy and dry
I wonder why, I wonder why
Oh so high in the sky.

Lisshan Rasakumaran (10)

SOS

The boiling huge sun
And around it, Earth runs
That's why living on Earth is so fun.

Our neighbouring planets
So empty and quiet
And I'm playing my clarinet
And worried about climate.

We should look after Earth
After plants and our oceans
Like our mums giving birth
We have one mother named Earth.

And for all the pollution
Which is destroying our land
We must find a solution
Before we all turn into sand.

Adele Aman Dosalieva (9)

The Dancer

The graceful, pretty dancer swept the floor with
her long, pink dress,
swaying side to side, always trying her best.
Moving about without a sound -
Practising and practising all day long;
determined to pass the long, hard test.
Smiling with teeth like diamonds;
mum standing near - emotional with one proud
tear.
As she disappears into the wonderful world of
dance,
she'll become the brightest star there has been for
years...
She knows to hide her fear.

Jessica Smart (8)

I Want To Be...

I want to be a mother
I want to be a father
I want to be anything I can be

I want to be a marine biologist
I want to be an archaeologist
I want to be anything I can be

I want to be a dentist
I want to be a chemist
I want to be anything I can be

I want to be an author
I want to be a teacher
I want to be anything I can be

I want to be a barrister
I want to be a solicitor
I want to be anything I can be.

Aryaan Mahmood (9)

Out Of This World

O h my, it's time to start our
U tterly amazing adventure
T ime to zoom into

O ther crazy
F antasy planets

T alented, singing biscuits
H umming to
I ncredible pieces of music
S ecretly chewing on the

W orld's delicious gum
O bedient ice cream carefully making
R aspberry cake
L aughing in the kitchen
D inner will be soon!

Aysha Afridi (11)

Attention Thief

The whole nation stares at me
For me it is a little bit creepy
Sometimes I wonder what am I
I just know that one day I will die

I make you scared
I make you cry
I make you laugh
Without my knowledge you would be daft

Sometimes I am fuzzing
But mostly I am clear
I consume your attention
People hold me dear

I am not the one
Who is being ruled
Be grateful about how
My imprisoned characters inspire you.

Abarnaya Jeyaseelan (10)

The End

The end of the world is near,
The plastic won't disappear,
This is the end.

We betrayed Mother Nature's care,
This is not fair,
This is the end.

Animals are endangered,
Sealife choking on plastic scattered,
This is the end.

The trees we cut, break and bend,
Are permanently damaged no apology we send.
This is the end.
So please, take care of nature's beauty,
If not,
This is the end.

Shyaama Modha (11)

Idealistic Introvercy

There is a planet far far away
Where I go daily to relax and play
It's filled with fun,
Animals, books and sun.
It is my eternal escape.

The most beautiful planet, just for me
That will remain there for eternity
Hanging upside down
Looking like a clown
Engrossed in my imaginary world.

When life gets busy, and I need to withdraw,
I fly to my planet so I can fully ignore
The stimulating, sociable life I behold
That I need to escape to find my mould.
This is my idealistic introvercy!

Ione Greenstock (10)

Animals

Animals are cute
Animals are tall
Animals are furry
Some big, some small

Hedgehogs are small
Giraffes are tall
Rabbits are furry
They're all big and small

Animals are rough
Animals are strong
Animals are fast
We can't name them all

Animals like us are big and small
There are so many
That's why I love them all

Animals are fun
Animals can run
I will read this to everyone.

Amelia Spahia

There Is Only One World

There is only one Earth,
Have you ever seen litter on the floor,
This litter is our planet's worth,
The more you throw away the more it hurts the environment,
Each little atom of plastic can last 100 years,
The amount of waste out there is just an embarrassment,
The world's population is showing the world abandonment,
Please help by not littering,
You may be bringing the planet to its end,
Pollution, littering, global warming,
They make the world grey,
There is only one world!

Zayan Hussain (10)

Parents, The Fruits

Parents are like sweet mangoes, their fragrance fills the home
Parents are like apples, if you have them you don't need doctors
Parents are like dates, full of sweetness
Parents are like kiwi, full of vitality
Parents are like watermelon, cools you down
Parents are like oranges, necessity of life
Parents are like bananas, boosts you when run down
Parents are like coconuts, helps with everything
Parents are like pomegranates, have greatness.

Maanav Nagda (11)

Life In Space

Wow, space! What a wonderful place.
It's like a dream, it just makes me beam.
Space, it's such a sight, luckily the aliens don't bite.
The stars elegantly twinkle, just like a stardust sprinkle!
It's so very peaceful but also very beautiful.
It's so silent so there's no reason to be violent!
Because the sky is sparkling is seems so startling.
When it's so amazing it gets me gazing.
Now my mission is accomplished.

Leila Smith (9)

I Dreamt

I dreamt I was touching the white fluffy clouds
I dreamt I was standing on the large bumpy moon
I dreamt I landed on the sparkly bright stars
I dreamt I sat on Mars looking out to space
I dreamt I looked at the beauty of the rainbow
I dreamt I walked around Jupiter saying what a
beautiful planet it was
I dreamt there were magnificent, golden rays
coming into my eyes
I dreamt I painted a smile on the sun for everybody
to see and smile!

Fatima Akmal (8)

From The Window

As I sit by the window,
Looking outside,
I see cars, a few people
And birds streaming by.
There is Dad and his friend,
Testing bikes down the road,
And there comes a car
With a big, hefty load.

Even though all the laws
Say: "You must stay at home"
They are broken as if they are
All made of foam.

So those are the things I can
See from my window,
Sitting here, writing these words.
Sitting and watching,
Sitting and watching,
Sitting and watching the birds.

Matvei Nepomnjastsih

Broken Hearts

Bullying is a harmful thing,
Because you lack the peace within,
Young people dying at a young age,
Broken by hearts filled with rage,

It started off as teasing,
But then the words had meaning,
The kind that made them silent,
Then you resorted to violence,

But why do you cause people such pain,
After all you have nothing to gain,
People are committing suicide,
If you don't stop, they will die!

Khadijah Iman (8)

The Time Continuum

In the time continuum planets lie
In three dimensions of space
Here, far and wide

Here in the Milky Way
Eight planets lie
One sun remains
And loads of stars cascade

The dwarf planet lies the furthest away
Nicknamed the goblin
So people say

In one dimension
The widest one
Nowhere near the blazing sun
Lies an extraterrestrial
In a spaceship zooming about having fun.

Xander Weston (8)

In The Sky Above

Glistening in the sky above,
Lie billions of stars, more than enough
Stars that are made of magma and fire
Packs a spectacular view, don't call me a liar

Glistening in the sky above
Lie dozens of planets, more than enough
Planets that are made of stone and ice
Packs a spectacular view, amazingly nice

Glistening in the sky above
Lies unknown things, more than enough
Who knows the endless space out there
The universe will never end, to be fair.

Rashvin

MacBeth

MacBeth the killer
Stalks forward with thoughts of death
He raises his knife
Regicide committed by
MacBeth, thane of Glamis

Duncan the noble
Murdered by his most trusted
And he is the King
The fair and decent Scottish King
Murdered by MacBeth

MacBeth has murdered
The lowly, sore assassin
This terrible crime
Which must be dealt with harshly
For MacBeth is a bad man.

Malakaai Luke Steele (11)

Year 6 Goes Wrong

This is seriously not funny.
You're being very rude.
Sarah no throwing food.
Now sit down it's reading time.
Yes Rafi your spelling is sublime.
Let's read The Gruffalo, nah you're too old.
No Alex, don't you dare eat that mould!
You just had break time, can't you wait?
Having to scream at you I really do hate.
Sam your arms are very long.
Great, another day in Year 6 goes wrong.

Teddy Epstein (10)

The Petrifying Monster

I once saw something that was
As round as a football
As big as the sun
And don't get me started on its long trunk
It was as lengthy as a giraffe's neck
And its tummy was scarlet red
Its eyes were shiny pearls
Its claws were as sticky as toffee
And don't even remind me of its hollow mouth
But it had the sweet smell of bluebells
And the melodious voice of a nightingale
And the pure heart of gold
And guess what!
We became best friends!

Yahia Abdulgawad (7)

Outer Space

Outer space, outer space, how things fly by
Comets and stars like UFOs that illuminate the sky
Black holes and white holes sucking things and
spitting things nearby
Oh my! Oh my! Look at the beautiful night sky.

Outer space, outer space, how you marvel me
Full moon or crescent, every day you cradle me
Far, far away, creating illusions in the sky
Outer space, outer space, an incredible sight.

Rayan Anderson (9)

Stars

I gaze at stars late into the night,
Shiny shooting stars all pearly white.
The sky a blanket of navy blue,
Cheeks red with happiness gazing with my best friend Sue.
My eyes start to drop at the endless sky,
What wonderful adventures, oh my!
I fall into a dream all about stars and my favourite pie.
She carries me up high into the house with a tired sigh,
She hugs me close and whispers goodbye!

Olivia Peddle (11)

Save This Planet!

Stop killing creatures,
With new and intelligent features.
Stop wasting water,
And stop all this slaughter.
Stop using plastic,
This would be fantastic!
Don't make more mess,
Try to make less.
Don't cause global warming,
People give these warnings.
Let's make a better planet,
To make this world more clear,
Let's make it better,
For others will be here.

Chudi Patrick Onwuokwu (9)

What I Saw In Space

I saw an alien in space,
Floating in a floating race.
I saw a spaceman in a rocket,
With a toothbrush in his pocket.

I saw a sandwich in space,
Backflipping all over the place.
I don't expect too much from Mars,
There are no coffee shops or bars.

In the brightly shining stars,
There might be coffee jars.
That is the end,
Maybe next time friend.

Shayaan Noman (8) & Safa

Success

The world revolves around one thing - success
Success is believing in yourself
Success is not giving up
Success is believing in what you can do
Success does not have full stops but only commas
Everyone has their way of achieving success
Success is defined not only by wins
But how you recover when you fall
It's all in the mind
Success is not a destination
Success is a journey.

Ashrit Marti (11)

When I Grow Up

When I grow up it goes like this
When I grow up I'll be an inventor
Just like the one down the street
Who I like to meet
I ask my sister what do you want to be
She says that she would like to be me
So I ask my mum what do you want to be
She says she wants to be a singer
So again I ask my dad what do you want to be
He says he wants to be a ringer
But what do you want to be?

Aarya Goenka (10)

Space

I took up in the sky
I wonder how high?
Then in my face
I see the signs of space!

I see the planets circling the sun
Like everybody wanting a hot cross bun!
I observe the land on the moon
I know I'm going to run out of oxygen soon.

As I float upwards I see
The powerful force gravity
Is gradually pulling me upwards
Where there are a lot of hazards.

Maryam Hooria Maqsood (10)

Animal Mad Me

I love animals
So cute and furry
Dogs so friendly
While lions so deadly
Monkeys that are very pecky
While crocodiles are so murky
Cats are playful
Tigers so preyful
Fish are so fascinating
Wile oarfish are so revolting
Hatchet fish and anglerfish glow so bright
While colossal squid can grow to a very big height
Well, that's the end of my animal poem.

Riya Boominathan (8)

Bullies

Bullies are so hard to love,
Because they push and shove.

Calling people names makes you sad,
If it carries on it can make you mad.

They can make you feel all alone,
So it's good to have a place to moan.

If the bully has given you a poke,
A friend can help by telling a joke!

A friend can make you smile,
By being with you for a while.

A bully can make you want to hide,
People help by taking your side.

Harry Fielden (8)

Google Eyes

Google eyes, you can put them anywhere
To apples, fruit and vegetables
Google eyes are everywhere.

Google eyes you can put them anywhere
To bags, clothes, any other household items
Google eyes are everywhere

This is getting annoying so one last time
Google eyes you can put them anywhere
To cats, dogs, any other animal
Google eyes are everywhere!

Emma Timis (10)

Death

Death is dark and pitch-black,
It smells like the rotting flesh on a corpse,
Death tastes like a throbbing bile explosion
in the throat,
It sounds like a woman in agony screaming
for help.
Death feels like a cold infectious disease, crawling
up the body,
It looks like the Grim Reaper riding a fire-breathing
dragon,
Death comes alive at the end of our lives.

Amar Maan (10)

Be Kind

God made the world
In a wise condition
He moulded clay
In all sorts of colours

But now his creation
Has turned on the others
Some of the clay
Is defeating the other colours

Remember that creed and colour don't matter
What matters is your actions
Your differences are nothing in the world
But your goodness matters most.

Razi Shabeeh (7)

Space

S upermassive black hole at the centre of every galaxy.

P lanets of many colours made of rocks and gases reflecting the sun at different times.

A stronauts approaching in their modules as they explore the edge of the universe.

C old Neptune still warmer than the Boomerang Nebula.

E arth is the source of life as we know it, but for how long?

Sam Toffel (7)

My Adventurous Ride In The Woods

I went for an adventurous ride in the woods
I thought I met a cute bear
Guess how did it look...
Definitely not like in a book,
It was a big black furry smelly bear!

I went for an adventurous ride in the woods
I thought I met a mysterious dinosaur
Guess how did it look...
Definitely not like in a book
It wasn't a huge spiky back dinosaur,
But it was a tiny spiky back chameleon!

Khushi Rohit (6)

Crazy Hair

There was a girl called Claire,
With black and curly crazy hair!
It was hard to brush
She couldn't do it in a rush.
It was even worse when she got out of bed
So she tied it in a ribbon on top of her head.
When she washed it in the shower,
It stuck up like the Eiffel Tower.
Then she shaved her hair,
And her head was very bare.

Lily-May Spence (8)

Heaven, Sweet Heaven

Heaven, sweet heaven
A place of awe
What would you want more?
Heaven, sweet heaven
Angels are singing
Bells are ringing
Heaven, sweet heaven
Love is in the air
Unicorns everywhere
Heaven, sweet heaven
Heavenly feeling
Soul healing
Heaven, sweet heaven
Doves in the sky
Beautiful and happy, oh my.

Oliwia Zborowska (10)

Out Of This World

The world spins round in a pace
Even slower than a running race
We have loads of different planets
And also orange carrots
When people go to the moon or space
They are called astronauts
But when they are in a rocket
Their minds are scared like a jigsaw
This is the end of my poem today
And I hope you have a great day.

Neive Sarah Homewood (11)

I Love My Mum As A Fairy

I love my mum
She likes a juicy plum
She is a fairy
But her name is not Mary
She has a cat
Who scratches a mat
She has a daughter
Who likes to fly
She has a castle
With a big rascal
I love my mum
She hates to hum
She hated dogs
The one that jogs
I love my mum
She likes a juicy plum.

Sumayyah Ayub

The Moon And The Sun

As the moon said to the sun,
Why am I not as light?
As the sun said to the moon,
My heat you can't fight.

As the moon said to the sun,
My job's way more fun.
As the sun said to the moon,
But I can see cars not stars.

As the moon said to the sun,
You are lonely because I have planet friends.

Daniel Park (10)

I Wish

I wish I could be small enough
to wear a foxglove for a hat
I wish I could wear a snail's shell
to protect me from angry words
I wish I could hide inside a snowflake
and drift off to somewhere magical
I wish I could be a lion
as I could protect my feelings
I wish I could be Jamie
to be happy every day.

Evangeline Goodwin (8)

The Snowman

I made myself a snowman
As perfect as can be.
I made him look very neat
But also very smart.
I told him my true wish,
He granted it for me!
I was suddenly surprised,
And realised I could fly!
I thanked him very much,
And let him sleep with me.
I made him some pyjamas, and a pillow for his head.
Last night he ran away, but first he wet my bed!

Yixing Chen (9)

When I Saw A Monster

When I saw a monster,
His face was green and his eyes were red.
When I saw a monster,
His teeth were black and his nose was yellow.
When I saw a monster,
His nails were brown and his hair was orange.
When I saw a monster,
His legs were pink and his mouth was purple.
When you see a monster,
Run!

Ali Mian (7)

Tom Moore

T om Moore
O nwards he goes
M oore by name, more by nature

M oving on doing his 100 laps of his garden
O verjoyed with the money donated
O h my, it's at 20 million!
R emarkable dedication up the money goes
E veryone is supporting Tom Moore.

Amber Williamson-Brown (9)

Truth

Truth is fun
Truth is beautiful
If you don't have truth, you'll have none,
World relies on truth
Trust relies on truth
Friendship relies on truth
Everything relies on truth
Truth hurts but silence kills
Truth is a pathless land
Truth is the substance of morality
Truth is the ultimate power
Quickly say it louder.

Aarush Marti (8)

Dragons

Dragons breathe fire
And they are liars
Dragons can burn
Dragons can earn
A roast meal
Dragons can make deals
Dragons look like dinosaurs
Dragons look like pterosaurs
Dinosaurs can stomp
Dragons can fly
So don't get muddled up
With dinosaurs and dragons.

Anujan Nirubaraj (9)

The Raging Sea

I could tell that the sea despised me,
As it screamed, it lay down a bed of foam upon me
I had been attacked by a frothing dog.
Each wave reached to push me into the dark
Depths of the ocean.
Growing stronger and stronger.
The raging cyan blue waves leapt over me,
Letting out a roar,
Swallowing me whole.

Mohammed Sulevani (10)

Magpie

M agpies are elegant but squeaky
A bird with a tail long and velvety
G ems and lustrous things they adore
P ut one outside and they'll pick for sure
I mpish habits under a plumage black and white
E erie looks but with a brain so bright!

Fareed Ahmed (6)

Hogwarts

W easleys are redheads

I 'm a wizard that goes to Hogwarts

Z *ap!* Someone got jinxed

A zkaban is a place nobody wants to be in

R on and Harry met on a train

D raco Malfoy is a bad wizard and arch-nemesis to Harry!

Muhmmad Ayub (9)

My Dogs

White, white, black and white,
Every good emotion.
Born on Halloween,
Ghost dog cute.
Cute adorable baby werewolf
Loves tummy tickles, twitch and sneeze.
Terrible stink bombs, cuddly cute.
Big ole teddy bear, lumpydump Boo.
Boo Bear, Pipi, and Lupeyloo.
Altogether, fun, fun, whoo!

Finn Gooding (8)

What Is Love?

Love
As innocent as a dove
Sweet as honey
Involves no money
Only two hearts
That will never drift apart
There's no fights
Just calm nights
A warm feeling
Just makes everything more appealing
Love is just as innocent as a dove.

Mariam Khan (14)

My Daddy (Pancake Head)

I am Tiger, middle name Lily
I love my daddy, he is silly
We like cowboys and milkshakes
We are ninjas that eat pancakes
It's fun for us to ride on boats
And at the farm to feed the goats
He will take me fishing soon
He loves me to the moon.

Tiger Eaton (6)

The Rocket Out Of Control

Dashing through space in a rocket,
Flying past Earth, Mars and Jupiter,
Bang, stars broke with glitter flying out like fireworks,
The rocket was out of control,
Then aliens swung by and came back to look,
They were eating pizza and watching the out of control rocket.

Louie Trett (7)

Afterlife

What happens when we die
Do we go to hell because we lie?
Will I live somewhere nice
Or will I only get a grain of rice?

Will I get another chance
Or will I go into a trance?
Is heaven a good place
Or will I die because I get a case?

Sianna Cooper (10)

Shooting Star

I'm a twinkling light in the sky at night
I'm a tiny snowdrop next to the moon
I'm a jewel so far
I'm a scar across the black sky
I'm a shining diamond on a wall of black
I'm a wish still waiting
I'm a shooting star.

Harvey Goodsell

Happy Days

Very beautiful is the river
Very graceful as it shimmers
Blue, calm and always bright
It's as beautiful as a colourful kite
The river is always there for me
So we both agreed
To help each other hand in wave
They were those happy days.

Madison Porter

Dinosaur

Dinosaurs fight
They also turn on the lights
Dinosaurs, dinosaurs, dinosaurs,
They're too busy
And the juice they drink is juicy
Dinosaurs stomp so loud
It makes the world shake
Dinosaur vs dinosaur fight
One dinosaur wins.

Anujan Nirubaraj (9)

Out Of This World

You should not bully
It is very mean
You make people cry
Even though we try not to
So please don't use horrible words
As these do hurt our feelings
Believe in yourself and others
So please be true
As we all should do.

Charlie West (7)

Pearl Panda

Pearl is a cute fluffy panda bear
She hates cheating in games and likes to play fair
Her favourite food to eat is bamboo
She doesn't like being locked in the zoo
Pearl is my favourite panda of all
Because she is so very small.

Shannon Carol Briggs (11)

I Feel Bad For My Feet

I feel bad for my feet
My feet are carrying my body
My body is carrying my head
My head is carrying my brain
My brain is carrying my grey cells
My grey cells are carrying my knowledge
My knowledge is carrying the world
Gosh, I feel bad for my feet.

Rosie Shindler (8)

My Shadow

A kennings poem

A day-stalker
An eye-catcher
A sun-crawler
A competitive-monster
A puppet-creator
A weaponless assassinator
An illuminated terror
An opposite-walker
A silent killer
A no-faced horror
An awoken creature
A disturbed predator...

Oreoluwapo Faseha (10)

Anxiety

Stomach lurching
Brain moving as fast as I
Read my work to the class
Cheeks burning
Minds calling
Tapping pens
Fast pacing
Freezing in place
This is just a case of anxiety.

Jayden Tomlinson (11)

Unicorn Land!!!

Unicorn Land is where unicorns stay,
Unicorns play,
Unicorns lay,
Unicorns eat rainbow hay.

Unicorn Land is where unicorns run,
Unicorns have fun,
Unicorns are a tonne,
Unicorns love the ice cream sun!

Davina Bajwa (11)

I Can See Spring Everywhere

Goodbye winter
Spring is here
I can see flowers everywhere
Blossoms are blooming
Birds are singing
Fairies are playing
Bees are buzzing
I can see spring everywhere.

Celio Carreiro-Lee (9)

The Wonders And Secrets Of Space

Space
Humongous, starry
Glistening, amazing, scintillating
Wonderous, hulking... monotonous, piddling
Frightening, fading, disintegrating
Squandered, polluted
Earth.

Amr Abdulgawad (10)

Space

Out of the Earth where never to have been,
Aliens and monsters are always very mean,
Every little child has that fear that an alien is to be
seen,
Aliens have been seen green.

Monica Bajwa (9)

Elephant

E lephants

L urking

E verywhere

P laying

H ot cross buns

A nd

N aming

T rees.

Elsha Jom (8)

Mary Seacole Limerick

There was a woman called Mary
She never found anything scary
She went on a tour
To nurse in the war
The soldiers were grateful and cheery.

Kayla Thompson (9)

YOUNG WRITERS INFORMATION

We hope you have enjoyed reading this book – and that you will continue to in the coming years.

If you're a young writer who enjoys reading and creative writing, or the parent of an enthusiastic poet or story writer, do visit our website **www.youngwriters.co.uk**. Here you will find free competitions, workshops and games, as well as recommended reads, a poetry glossary and our blog. There's lots to keep budding writers motivated to write!

If you would like to order further copies of this book, or any of our other titles, then please give us a call or order via your online account.

Young Writers
Remus House
Coltsfoot Drive
Peterborough
PE2 9BF
(01733) 890066
info@youngwriters.co.uk

Join in the conversation!
Tips, news, giveaways and much more!

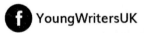 YoungWritersUK    @YoungWritersCW